Puzzles for 4

Complete the number grids by filling in missing numbers.

1

12	+	4	=	
−	■	+	■	−
10	−		=	8
=	■	=	■	=
2	+	6	=	

2

	+	11	=	16
+	■	+	■	+
6	+		=	9
=	■	=	■	=
11	+	14	=	

3

	+	9	=	13
+	■	−	■	+
10	−		=	7
=	■	=	■	=
14	+	6	=	

4

3	×		=	12
×	■	×	■	×
3	×	2	=	
=	■	=	■	=
	×	8	=	72

Grids galore

Complete the number grids by filling in the missing numbers.

1

5	+	6	=	
+	■	−	■	+
4	−		=	1
=	■	=	■	=
	+	3	=	

2

8	+		=	10
+	■	−	■	+
	−	0	=	7
=	■	=	■	=
	+	2	=	

3

	+	4	=	8
−	■	÷	■	−
2	×		=	
=	■	=	■	=
	+	2	=	

4

	−	13	=	1
+	■	+	■	+
8	−		=	3
=	■	=	■	=
	−	18	=	4

Jungle maths

Complete the number grids by filling
in the missing numbers.

1

3	+		=	12
×		×		÷
	÷	2	=	6
=		=		=
36	÷		=	2

2

2	×	6	=	
+		−		−
	−	1	=	2
=		=		=
5	+		=	10

3

15	÷	3	=	
−		×		+
3	−	2	=	
=		=		=
	−	6	=	6

4

	−	16	=	3
+		−		+
2	+		=	14
=		=		=
21	−	4	=	

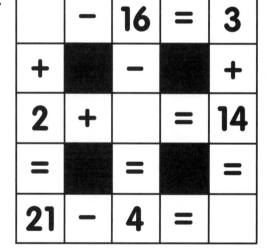

Helicopter sums

Do the sums, then write the answers as words
to complete the crossword.

a → $4 + 3 =$ **b** $16 \div 8 =$ **d** $6 - 6 =$ **f** $7 + 4 =$

a ↓ $8 \times 2 =$ **c** $5 + 3 =$ **e** $10 \div 10 =$

Busy number bees

Complete the number grids by filling in the missing numbers.

1

7	−	6	=	
+	■	−	■	+
1	+		=	3
=	■	=	■	=
8	−	4	=	

2

7	+	4	=	
×	■	−	■	+
3	×		=	9
=	■	=	■	=
21	−	1	=	

3

12	+	3	=	
−	■	×	■	÷
	−		=	5
=	■	=	■	=
6	−		=	3

4

	+	9	=	13
+	■	−	■	+
10	−		=	7
=	■	=	■	=
14	+	6	=	

Blowing bubbles

Complete the number grids by filling in the missing numbers.

1

12	+	4	=	
−	■	+	■	−
10	−		=	8
=	■	=	■	=
2	+	6	=	

8

2

2	+		=	10
−	■	−	■	−
	+	2	=	3
=	■	=	■	=
1	+	6	=	

3

	+	11	=	16
+	■	+	■	+
6	+		=	9
=	■	=	■	=
11	+	14	=	

3

4

3	+	6	=	
+	■	−	■	−
2	+		=	6
=	■	=	■	=
	−	2	=	3

7

Messy maths

Do the sums, then write the answers as words to complete the crossword.

a 4 × 2 =   **c→** 9 + 5 =   **d** 20 ÷ 10 =

b 20 ÷ 4 =   **c↓** 20 × 2 =   **e** 7 + 3 =

Underwater sums

Complete the number grids by filling in the missing numbers.

1

6	−		=	5
+	■	×	■	+
2	×		=	
=	■	=	■	=
8	−	1	=	7

2

	×	2	=	6
+	■	−	■	−
1	×		=	
=	■	=	■	=
4	+		=	5

3

5	−		=	2
+	■	÷	■	+
	×	3	=	
=	■	=	■	=
	+	1	=	8

4

4	+		=	6
×	■	−	■	+
	+	1	=	
=	■	=	■	=
8	+	1	=	

Number creatures

Complete the number grids by filling in the missing numbers.

1

4	×	4	=	
÷	■	÷	■	÷
2	×		=	8
=	■	=	■	=
	×	1	=	2

2

4	+		=	16
+	■	+	■	−
	−	2	=	
=	■	=	■	=
18	−		=	4

3

6	+		=	8
÷	■	+	■	+
	−	1	=	
=	■	=	■	=
3	×	3	=	9

4

4	+		=	9
×	■	+	■	×
	−		=	2
=	■	=	■	=
12	+		=	18

Shipwrecked maths

Look in this wordsearch for the answers
to these sums.

9 x 9 =   2 x 3 =   4 x 1 =

50 − 33 =   6 + 10 =   140 − 110 =

21 ÷ 7 =   100 ÷ 10 =

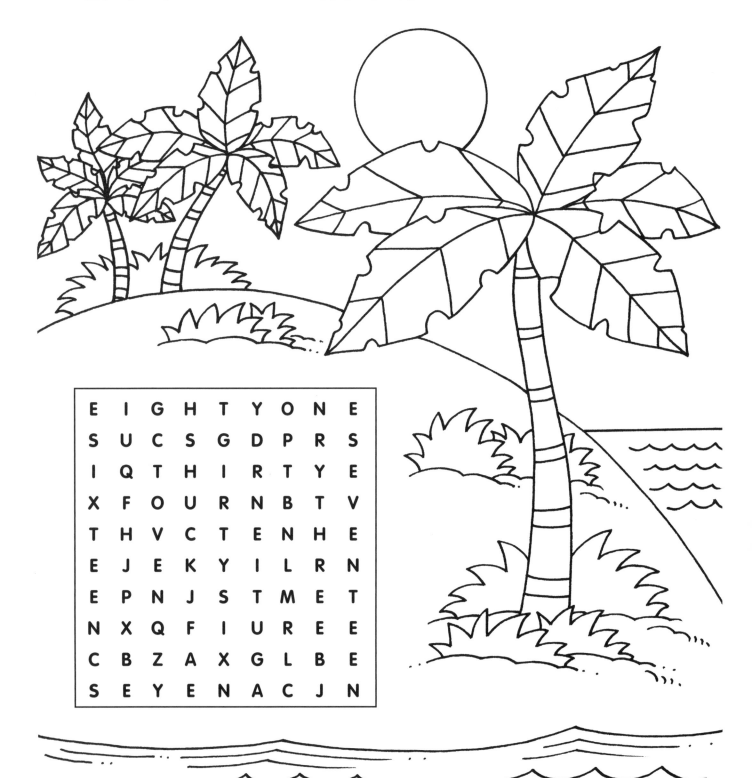

```
E  I  G  H  T  Y  O  N  E
S  U  C  S  G  D  P  R  S
I  Q  T  H  I  R  T  Y  E
X  F  O  U  R  N  B  T  V
T  H  V  C  T  E  N  H  E
E  J  E  K  Y  I  L  R  N
E  P  N  J  S  T  M  E  T
N  X  Q  F  I  U  R  E  E
C  B  Z  A  X  G  L  B  E
S  E  Y  E  N  A  C  J  N
```

Monkeys' maths

Do the sums, then write the answers as words
to complete the crossword.

a → 3 x 3 =   **b** 5 + 3 =   **d** 10 − 2 =

a ↓ 11 + 8 =   **c** 6 x 3 =   **e** 4 x 4 =

Lift off!

Complete the number grids by filling in the
missing numbers.

Ski maths

Look in this wordsearch for the answers to these sums.

$6 \times 11 =$ $9 \times 9 =$ $46 - 39 =$

$23 + 48 =$ $33 \div 3 =$ $26 - 22 =$

$20 \div 4 =$ $14 + 16 =$

S	I	X	T	Y	S	I	X	A
E	B	Z	C	U	D	P	R	E
V	Q	S	F	X	V	G	T	A
E	L	E	V	E	N	B	H	D
N	H	V	C	I	F	H	I	G
T	J	E	K	W	I	L	R	O
Y	P	N	J	Q	T	M	T	F
O	X	Q	F	O	U	R	Y	I
N	V	R	L	S	K	U	P	V
E	I	G	H	T	Y	O	N	E

Batty sums

Do the sums, then write the answers as words
to complete the crossword.

a 50 ÷ 5 =

b 99 ÷ 9 =

c 3 × 3 =

d 45 + 7 =

e ↓ 4 + 12 =

e → 28 ÷ 4 =

f 150 ÷ 50 =

g 6 × 2 =

h 1 × 1 =

Literary maths

Do the sums, then write the answers as words
to complete the crossword.

a 14 + 3 =
c 5 × 8 =
f 16 + 4 =

b↓ 15 ÷ 3 =
d 20 ÷ 10 =
g 30 ÷ 15 =

b→ 68 ÷ 17 =
e 90 ÷ 30 =
h 10 × 2 =

Crunching sums

Complete the number grids by filling in the missing numbers.

1

	+	7	=	8
+	■	–	■	+
9	–		=	
=	■	=	■	=
	+	5	=	15

2

8	–	4	=	
+	■	+	■	+
	–	2	=	3
=	■	=	■	=
13	–		=	7

3

13	–		=	3
+	■	–	■	+
	+	2	=	
=	■	=	■	=
20	–		=	12

4

	+	2	=	12
–	■	–	■	–
3	+		=	4
=	■	=	■	=
7	+	1	=	

Sums crossword

Do the sums, then write the answers as words
to complete the crossword.

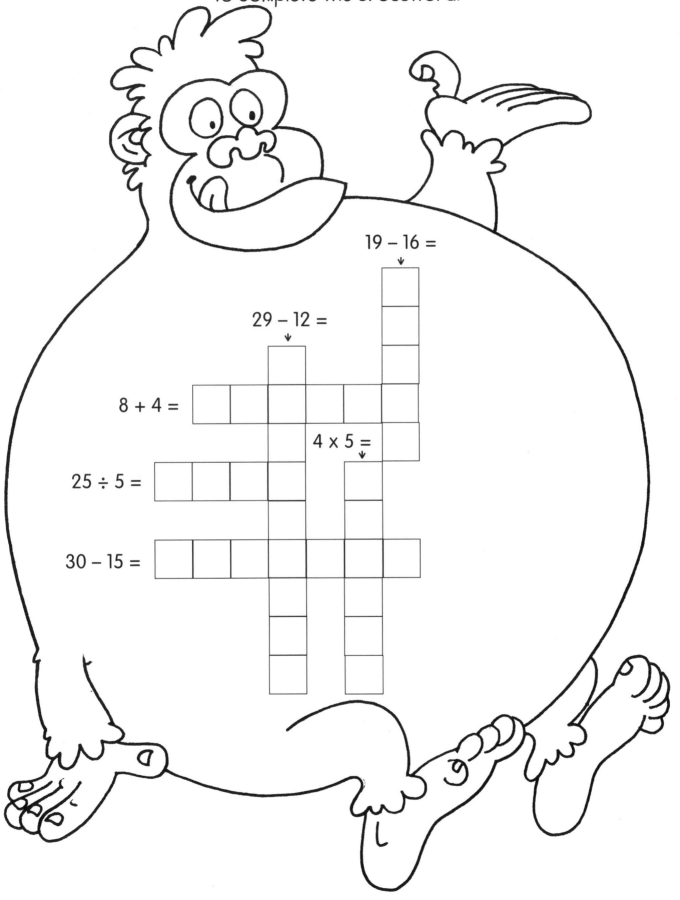

19 − 16 =

29 − 12 =

8 + 4 =

4 x 5 =

25 ÷ 5 =

30 − 15 =

Mexican maths

Look in this wordsearch for the answers to these sums.

6 x 7 =   34 + 65 =   14 + 25 =

56 ÷ 8 =   25 x 2 =   94 − 85 =

23 − 9 =   60 ÷ 3 =

T F O U R T E E N

H O Q W E T Y U I

I R I O P A S D N

R T W E N T Y X E

T Y F G H J K L T

Y T Z N F I F T Y

N W C I V B M Q N

I O W N E R T Y I

N U I E S E V E N

E A D G J D S B E

Mole hill maths

Complete the number grids by filling in the missing numbers.

1

2	+		=	12
+	■	−	■	+
	−	3	=	
=	■	=	■	=
9	+		=	16

2

12	+		=	14
−	■	+	■	−
	−	2	=	
=	■	=	■	=
4	+		=	8

3

4	+		=	12
+	■	−	■	+
	−	2	=	
=	■	=	■	=
14	+		=	20

4

10	+		=	16
−	■	+	■	−
	−	4	=	
=	■	=	■	=
5	+		=	15

Formula 1 maths

Do the sums, then write the answers as words
to complete the crossword.

a   20 − 11 =
b   6 + 5 =
c   150 ÷ 15 =

d   4 × 2 =
e   12 + 4 =
f   99 ÷ 9 =

g   144 ÷ 12 =
h   5 × 2 =
i   7 ÷ 7 =

Number squares

Complete the number grids by filling in the
missing numbers.

1

	+	2	=	12
+	■	−	■	+
7	−		=	5
=	■	=	■	=
17	−	0	=	

2

	−	3	=	6
+	■	−	■	+
2	+		=	4
=	■	=	■	=
11	−	1	=	

3

15	−		=	8
−	■	−	■	−
	−	3	=	2
=	■	=	■	=
10	−	4	=	

4

7	+		=	10
+	■	−	■	+
	−	2	=	5
=	■	=	■	=
14	+	1	=	

Animal magic

Complete the number grids by filling in the missing numbers.

1

	+	12	=	24
−	■	−	■	−
6	+	8	=	
=	■	=	■	=
	+	4	=	10

2

2	×		=	6
×	■	×	■	×
	×	1	=	
=	■	=	■	=
12	×		=	36

3

2	+	7	=	
+	■	−	■	−
2	+		=	7
=	■	=	■	=
	−	2	=	2

4

	−	5	=	5
−	■	+	■	−
2	+		=	5
=	■	=	■	=
8	−	8	=	

Kitten maths

Do the sums, then write the answers as words
to complete the crossword.

a → 35 + 25 =
a ↓ 35 ÷ 5 =
b 30 ÷ 3 =

c 18 + 9 =
d 9 × 2 =
e 5 × 4 =

f 200 ÷ 100 =
g 50 + 22 =
h 21 − 4 =

Show-jumping sums

Look in this wordsearch for
the answers to these sums.

$49 \div 7 =$ $6 + 7 =$ $9 + 9 =$

$74 - 62 =$ $32 \div 8 =$ $16 \div 2 =$

$23 + 27 =$ $26 + 16 =$ $5 \times 4 =$

F	O	R	T	Y	T	W	O	Q
O	W	E	W	R	Y	U	T	P
U	A	S	E	D	E	G	H	S
R	J	X	L	C	I	V	I	E
N	Q	E	V	R	G	T	R	V
I	O	P	E	A	H	S	T	E
F	I	F	T	Y	T	F	E	N
K	L	B	C	D	E	R	E	W
E	I	G	H	T	E	S	N	J
A	N	T	W	E	N	T	Y	K

Sailing maths

Do the sums, then write the answers as words to complete the crossword.

a 10 ÷ 2 =

b 17 + 43 =

c 25 − 6 =

d 5 + 3 =

e 10 × 5 =

f 30 ÷ 10 =

g 80 ÷ 8 =

h 7 ÷ 7 =

i 12 + 7 =

Magic maths

Do the sums, then write the answers as words
to complete the crossword.

a 21 − 13 =

b 45 ÷ 9 =

c 13 + 7 =

d 150 ÷ 50 =

e ➤ 30 − 11 =

e ↓ 36 ÷ 4 =

f 43 + 27 =

g 22 − 11 =

h 100 ÷ 10 =

i 5 − 4 =

Number fun

Complete the number grids by filling
in the missing numbers.

1

14	−		=	8
−	■	+	■	−
	+	4	=	
=	■	=	■	=
12	−		=	2

2

18	−		=	16
−	■	+	■	−
4	+	2	=	
=	■	=	■	=
	−		=	10

3

16	−		=	13
−	■	+	■	+
	−	7	=	
=	■	=	■	=
6	+		=	16

4

3	+		=	10
+	■	−	■	+
8	−		=	
=	■	=	■	=
	+	4	=	15

Cheesy sums

Complete the number grids by filling
in the missing numbers.

1

5	+		=	12
+	■	+	■	+
4	+		=	
=	■	=	■	=
	+	12	=	

2

5	+	6	=	
+	■	−	■	+
	−	4	=	3
=	■	=	■	=
	+	2	=	

3

	+	8	=	
+	■	−	■	+
6	−		=	2
=	■	=	■	=
12	+		=	16

4

8	+		=	10
+	■	−	■	+
8	−	2	=	
=	■	=	■	=
	+	0	=	

Disco maths

Do the sums, then write the answers as words
to complete the crossword.

a → 50 − 20 =   **c** 4 × 3 =   **f** 8 × 5 =
a ↓ 3 × 7 =   **d** 20 × 4 =   **g** 21 − 10 =
b 100 ÷ 4 =   **e** 5 × 3 =   **h** 1000 ÷ 100 =

Festive maths

Look in this wordsearch for the answers to these sums.

$16 \div 8 =$ $13 + 12 =$ $32 - 11 =$

$20 \times 3 =$ $25 \div 5 =$ $3 \times 4 =$

$19 - 11 =$ $7 \times 6 =$

T	W	E	N	T	Y	O	N	E	E
W	A	V	B	W	L	C	M	I	I
E	N	D	X	O	E	W	P	G	G
N	F	Q	G	Y	H	Z	I	H	H
T	J	S	I	X	T	Y	K	T	T
Y	L	A	M	R	B	N	S	C	C
F	O	R	T	Y	T	W	O	F	F
I	O	D	P	F	Q	E	R	I	I
V	G	T	W	E	L	V	E	V	V
E	S	H	J	T	I	U	K	E	E

Answers

Puzzles for 4

1
12	+	4	=	16
−		+		−
10	−	2	=	8
=		=		=
2	+	6	=	8

2
5	+	11	=	16
+		+		+
6	+	3	=	9
=		=		=
11	+	14	=	25

3
4	+	9	=	13
+		−		+
10	−	3	=	7
=		=		=
14	+	6	=	20

4
3	×	4	=	12
×		×		×
3	×	2	=	6
=		=		=
9	×	8	=	72

Grids galore

1
5	+	6	=	11
+		−		+
4	−	3	=	1
=		=		=
9	+	3	=	12

2
8	+	2	=	10
+		−		+
7	−	0	=	7
=		=		=
15	+	2	=	17

3
4	+	4	=	8
−		÷		
2	×	2	=	4
=		=		=
2	+	2	=	4

4
14	−	13	=	1
+		+		+
8	−	5	=	3
=		=		=
22	−	18	=	4

Jungle maths

1
3	+	9	=	12
×		×		÷
12	÷	2	=	6
=		=		=
36	÷	18	=	2

2
2	×	6	=	12
+		−		−
3	−	1	=	2
=		=		=
5	+	5	=	10

3
15	÷	3	=	5
−		×		+
3	−	2	=	1
=		=		=
12	−	6	=	6

4
19	−	16	=	3
+		−		+
2	+	12	=	14
=		=		=
21	−	4	=	17

Helicopter sums

Across: s e v e n; t w o; e i g h t; o n e
Down: s i x t e e n; n o u g h t; e l e v e n; f i v e

Busy number bees

1
7	−	6	=	1
+		−		+
1	+	2	=	3
=		=		=
8	−	4	=	4

2
7	+	4	=	11
×		−		+
3	×	3	=	9
=		=		=
21	−	1	=	20

3
12	+	3	=	15
−		×		÷
6	−	1	=	5
=		=		=
6	−	3	=	3

4
4	+	9	=	13
+		−		+
10	−	3	=	7
=		=		=
14	+	6	=	20

Blowing bubbles

1
12	+	4	=	16
−		+		−
10	−	2	=	8
=		=		=
2	+	6	=	8

2
2	+	8	=	10
−		−		−
1	+	2	=	3
=		=		=
1	+	6	=	7

3
5	+	11	=	16
+		+		+
6	+	3	=	9
=		=		=
11	+	14	=	25

4
3	+	6	=	9
+		−		−
2	+	4	=	6
=		=		=
5	−	2	=	3

Messy maths

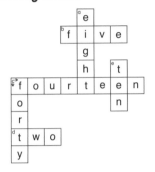

Across: f i v e; f o u r t e e n; t w o
Down: e i g h t; t e n; f o r t y

Underwater sums

1
6	−	1	=	5
+		×		+
2	×	1	=	2
=		=		=
8	−	1	=	7

2
3	×	2	=	6
+		−		+
1	×	1	=	1
=		=		=
4	+	1	=	5

3
5	−	3	=	2
+		÷		+
2	×	3	=	6
=		=		=
7	+	1	=	8

4
4	+	2	=	6
×		−		+
2	+	1	=	3
=		=		=
8	+	1	=	9

Number creatures

1
4	×	4	=	16
÷		÷		÷
2	×	4	=	8
=		=		=
2	×	1	=	2

2
4	+	12	=	16
+		+		−
14	−	2	=	12
=		=		=
18	−	14	=	4

3
6	+	2	=	8
÷		+		+
2	+	1	=	3
=		=		=
3	×	3	=	9

4
4	+	5	=	9
×		+		×
3	−	1	=	2
=		=		=
12	+	6	=	18

Shipwrecked maths

Word search: EIGHTYONE, SIXTEEN, THIRTY, FOUR, TEN, THREE, SIX, SEVENTEEN

Monkeys' maths

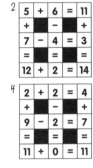

Across: n i n e; e i g h t; e i g h t e e n
Down: n i n e t e e n; e i g h t; s i x t e e n

Lift off!

1
9	×	2	=	18
−				÷
3	÷	1	=	3
=		=		=
6	×	1	=	6

2
5	+	6	=	11
+		−		+
7	−	4	=	3
=		=		=
12	+	2	=	14

3
10	×	2	=	20
÷		+		÷
5	−	1	=	4
=		=		=
2	+	3	=	5

4
2	+	2	=	4
+		−		+
9	−	2	=	7
=		=		=
11	+	0	=	11

Ski maths

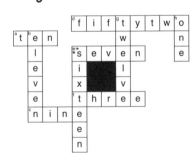

Word search: SIXTYSIX, ELEVEN, FOUR, EIGHTYONE, THIRTY, FORTYFIVE

Batty sums

Across: f i f t y t w o; s e v e n; t h r e e; n i n e
Down: t e n; o n e; t w e l v e; s i x; f i v e; s e v e n t e e n

Literary maths

Across: f o u r; t w o; s e v e n t e e n; f o r t y; t w e n t y
Down: f i v e; t e n; t w e n t y; t h r e e

Answers

Crunching sums

1

1	+	7	=	8
+		-		+
9	-	2	=	7
=		=		=
10	+	5	=	15

2

8	-	4	=	4
+		+		+
5	-	2	=	3
=		=		=
13	-	6	=	7

3

13	-	10	=	3
+		-		+
7	+	2	=	9
=		=		=
20	-	8	=	12

4

10	+	2	=	12
-		-		-
3	+	1	=	4
=		=		=
7	+	1	=	8

Number squares

1

10	+	2	=	12
+		-		+
7	-	2	=	5
=		=		=
17	-	0	=	17

2

9	-	3	=	6
+		-		+
2	+	2	=	4
=		=		=
11	-	1	=	10

3

15	-	7	=	8
-		-		-
5	-	3	=	2
=		=		=
10	-	4	=	6

4

7	+	3	=	10
+		-		+
7	-	2	=	5
=		=		=
14	+	1	=	15

Magic maths

Crossword solution: THREE, TEN, FIVE, NINETEEN, TWENTY (with SEVEN, ELEVEN, EIGHT, TWELVE intersecting)

Sums crossword

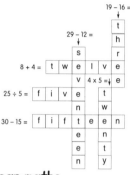

- 19 − 16 = THREE
- 29 − 12 = SEVENTEEN
- 8 + 4 = TWELVE
- 4 × 5 = TWENTY
- 25 ÷ 5 = FIVE
- 30 − 15 = FIFTEEN

Animal magic

1

12	+	12	=	24
-				-
6	+	8	=	14
=				=
6	+	4	=	10

2

2	×	3	=	6
×		×		×
6	×	1	=	6
=				=
12	×	3	=	36

3

2	+	7	=	9
+				-
2	+	5	=	7
=				=
4	-	2	=	2

4

10	-	5	=	5
-		+		-
2	+	3	=	5
=				=
8	-	8	=	0

Number fun

1

14	-	6	=	8
-		+		-
2	+	4	=	6
=		=		=
12	-	10	=	2

2

18	-	2	=	16
-		+		-
4	+	2	=	6
=		=		=
14	-	4	=	10

3

16	-	3	=	13
-		+		+
10	-	7	=	3
=		=		=
6	+	10	=	16

4

3	+	7	=	10
+		-		+
8	-	3	=	5
=		=		=
11	+	4	=	15

Mexican maths

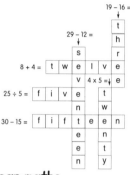

Word search containing: FOURTEEN, THIRTY, NINE, TWENTY, FIFTY, TWO, SEVEN

Kitten maths

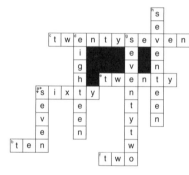

Crossword solution: TWENTY, SEVEN, TWENTY, SIXTY, TEN, TWO, EIGHT, SEVENTY

Cheesy sums

1

5	+		=	12
+		+		+
4	+		=	
=		=		=
	+	12	=	

2

5	+	6	=	11
+		-		+
7	-	4	=	3
=		=		=
12	+	2	=	14

3

6	+	8	=	14
+		-		+
6	-	4	=	2
=		=		=
12	+	4	=	16

4

8	+	2	=	10
+		-		+
8	-	2	=	6
=		=		=
16	+	0	=	16

Mole hill maths

1

2	+	10	=	12
+		-		+
7	-	3	=	4
=		=		=
9	+	7	=	16

2

12	+	2	=	14
-		+		-
8	-	2	=	6
=		=		=
4	+	4	=	8

3

4	+	8	=	12
+		-		+
10	-	2	=	8
=		=		=
14	+	6	=	20

4

10	+	6	=	16
-		+		-
5	-	4	=	1
=		=		=
5	+	10	=	15

Show-jumping sums

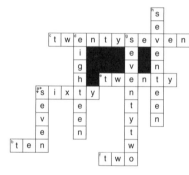

Word search containing: FORTY TWO, FOUR, FIFTY, EIGHT, TWENTY, THIRTEEN, SEVEN

Disco maths

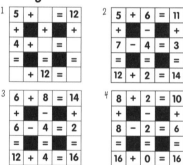

Crossword solution: FIFTEEN, THIRTY, TWENTY FIVE, TWELVE, TWELVE, TEN, and intersecting words (two, one, eight, twenty, etc.)

Formula 1 maths

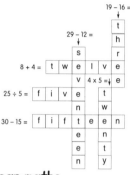

Crossword solution: EIGHT, TEN, ELEVEN, NINE, SIX, TWO, etc.

Sailing maths

Crossword solution: NINE, TEN, FIVE, EIGHT, THREE, SIXTY, NINETEEN, ONE, etc.

Festive maths

Word search containing: TWENTY ONE, SIXTY, FORTY TWO, TWELVE, TWENTY, EIGHT, FIVE